Once a W
Comprehension

Formerly 'Once a Week'

BOOK ONE

By HAYDN PERRY

Diploma in English Literature, University of London
formerly Headmaster, Merryhills School, Enfield

GINN AND COMPANY LTD

Without answers
Twenty-sixth impression 1988   058803
ISBN 0 602 20710 X

With answers
Ninth impression 1988   0.68802
ISBN 0 602 22420 9

Published by Ginn and Company Ltd
Prebendal House, Parson's Fee
Aylesbury, Bucks HP20 2QZ

Printed in Great Britain by
Blackmore Press Limited, Shaftesbury, Dorset

PREFACE

This book of English tests is intended for second-year pupils of Primary Schools. It can be used either for testing progress and ability, or it can serve as a textbook from which pupils can work alone or with the teacher's help.

In each of the thirty tests, the first question is of the comprehension type. These questions test the reading and reasoning of the pupils. More than sixty other types of questions are included in these books. All branches of English suitable for the age-group are thus adequately tested.

TO THE PUPIL

In each of the thirty tests there are five questions.

Read each question carefully, so that you understand exactly what you are asked to do before you begin.

Do not spend too long on any one question. You should answer all five questions in 45 minutes.

Make sure that you have not missed a question, or part of one.

If you find that you have made a mistake, alter your work clearly and neatly so that your teacher will know what it is you mean him to read and mark.

HAYDN PERRY

TEST 1

I. Read very carefully through the following passage, and then answer the questions.

The Tin Soldier

There were four-and-twenty tin soldiers, all brothers, for they had all been made from one old, tin spoon.   They wore red and blue uniforms, carried muskets in their arms, and held themselves very upright.

The first words they heard in the world, when the lid was taken off the box in which they lay, were "Tin soldiers!"   It was a little boy who said this, clapping his hands at the same time.   The soldiers had been given to him because it was his birthday.   He now set them out on the table.   The soldiers resembled each other to a hair, all except one who was rather different from the rest, for he had been made last, when there was not quite enough tin left.   He stood as firmly upon one tin leg as the others did upon two.

1. The soldiers were made from (*a*) a silver spoon; (*b*) a wooden spoon; (*c*) a tin spoon.   Which of these?
2. How do we know that they were all of one family?
3. What did the soldiers wear?
4. What did the little boy say?
5. Was he (*a*) unhappy; (*b*) not very interested; (*c*) very happy indeed?
6. Why was he given the soldiers?
7. Which part of one soldier was missing?
8. Why was this?
9. Which words tell us that the soldiers were **exactly alike**?
10. The one-legged soldier always (*a*) stood upright; (*b*) lay down on his back; (*c*) knelt beside the cannon.   Which of these?
11. Were the soldiers, when given to the little boy, (*a*) in a brown paper parcel; (*b*) in a plastic bag; (*c*) in a box?

II. The word **young** is opposite in meaning to the word **old**.

Example: The horse was **young,** but the dog was **old.**

Write out the sentences below using the opposite of the word in heavy type each time to fill the space:

1. Tom was **slow** at his work, but Jim was —— .
2. This book is **cheap,** but that one is —— .
3. Ann is **tall,** and Jane is —— .
4. Is your answer **right** or —— ?

III. **Punctuation marks** (, . ?) are missing from the following sentences. Write the sentences with the correct marks in them.
1. Where do you live
2. I want an axe a saw and a hammer
3. Do peas beans and carrots make a tasty meal
4. Can we buy ice lollies and lemonade at the fair

IV. **He** and **him** are words that are to do with MEN.   **She** and **her** are to do with WOMEN.

Change the following sentences that are about men, making them about women.

Example: 'My **father** is at home' becomes 'My **mother** is at home':

1. The **man** is in the park.
2. The **boy** rode the horse.
3. The **girl** bought a book.
4. The **widower** lived alone.

V. **Chop off its head.** If we chop the first letter off a **fruit**—PEAR, we get **that with which we hear**—EAR. (PEAR becomes EAR.)

Do the same with these:
1. 'A horse's home' becomes 'that at which we eat our meals'.
2. 'That with which we sweep' becomes 'part of any house'.
3. 'That from which we drink' becomes 'a girl'.
4. 'A dress' becomes 'something found in the earth'.

TEST 2

I. Read very carefully through the following passage, and then answer the questions.

The Lion and the Mouse

A lion was sleeping outside his den when a mouse, not knowing where he was going, ran over the mighty beast's nose and woke him. The lion clapped his paw upon the mouse and was about to make an end of him; but the mouse begged the lion to spare his life, and promised one day to pay him back for his kindness. So the lion let the mouse go.

Some time later, the lion found himself caught in a hunter's trap. He tried to free himself but could not do so. His roars echoed through the forest, and the mouse came running to see what was happening. He set to work to nibble through the net that held the lion prisoner, and in a short time he was able to set him free. In this way he repaid the great beast's kindness.

1. The mouse ran over the lion's nose (*a*) to show how brave he was; (*b*) to make the lion angry; (*c*) quite by accident. Which of these?
2. The lion was (*a*) prowling in the forest; (*b*) eating his prey; (*c*) sleeping peacefully. Which of these?
3. What did the lion mean to do with the mouse?
4. How did the mouse manage to make the lion set him free?
5. In which was the lion caught: (*a*) an iron cage; (*b*) a pit in the ground; (*c*) a net?
6. How did the mouse know that the lion was caught?
7. How did he set the lion free?
8. Which of these makes the best title for the story? (*a*) An Apple a Day Keeps the Doctor Away. (*b*) One Good Turn Deserves Another. (*c*) Empty Vessels Make the Most Sound.

II. Odd man out. In each of these groups of words, one word is out of place because it has nothing to do with the others.

Example: pen, pencil, ruler, **dog.** **Dog** is odd man out, for the others all have to do with writing.

Find the **odd man out** in these:

1. leg, arm, foot, paw
2. terrier, corgi, kitten, spaniel
3. cocoa, water, coffee, tea
4. rough, clean, neat, tidy

III. This is to **that.**

Example: **Finger** is to **hand,** as **toe** is to ——. Answer: **foot.**

Now do these:

1. **Little** is to **big,** as **short** is to ——.
2. **Dog** is to **puppy,** as **fox** is to ——.
3. **Tear** is to **sad,** as **laugh** is to ——.
4. **Oar** is to **boat,** as **pedal** is to ——.

IV. Here are the names of eight FRUITS. Write them down in **alphabetical order:** date, fig, apple, pear, raspberry, strawberry, banana, pineapple.

V. Look at the four letters: E D A L. With these four letters we can make several words. Here are some clues.

1. This is another name for a valley.
2. We do this when playing cards.
3. We find this inside pencils.

Now look at these four letters: E M N A. With these four letters we can make a number of words:

4. Christians say this at the end of a prayer.
5. A horse has one.
6. Everyone in the class has one.

TEST 3

I. Read very carefully through the following passage, and then answer the questions.

The Wolf and the Lamb

A wolf one day was drinking at a stream when he spied a lamb who was also refreshing herself farther down. The wolf made up his mind to eat the lamb, but he thought that he would find some excuse before doing so. He ran up to the lamb, and said, "How dare you muddy the water that I am drinking!" The lamb replied, "I do not see how that can be, since the water of the stream is running from you to me, and not from me to you."

The wolf then said, "Last year you called me many nasty names." "But that cannot be," replied the lamb, "for I was not born last year." "Then if it was not you, it was your father. It is no use making excuses," cried the wolf. With that he sprang upon the helpless lamb and devoured her.

1. How do we know that the wolf and the lamb were not standing in the stream side by side?
2. When the wolf saw the lamb, what did he make up his mind to do?
3. But what did he think he would do first?
4. The wolf said to the lamb: (a) "You are drinking all the water." (b) "I am afraid to come near the stream." (c) "You are making the water muddy for me." Which of these?
5. How did the lamb prove that the wolf was wrong?
6. The wolf then said: (a) "You broke into my den." (b) "You said unkind things about me." (c) "You stole some meat from me." Which of these is true?
7. How did the lamb show that this was untrue?
8. What happened to the lamb in the end?

II. The words in each of the following are in wrong order. Rearrange them to make sentences.

1. Barks dog the loudly.
2. Coat hangs the peg the on.
3. Boots school wore he to his.
4. Currant there's cake tea for.

III. What are these words? They each begin with WAR.

1. To sing like a bird.   WAR - - -
2. A soldier or fighting-man.   WAR - - - -
3. Where many rabbits live.   WAR - - -
4. A man who works in a prison.   WAR - - -
5. Part of any hospital.   WAR -

IV. The three words in the first bracket all have similar meanings. Choose **one word** from those in the second bracket that is also similar in meaning to those in the first bracket.

    Example: (**flock, herd, swarm**)—(thunder, **troop,** summer)

1. (sleek, velvety, smooth)—(glossy, ugly, rough)
2. (fog, mist, vapour)—(people, animals, cloud)
3. (jam, syrup, honey)—(timber, treacle, grass)
4. (mutter, mumble, murmur)—(whisper, cry, shout)

V. **How they do it.** One of the words in this list fits into each of the following sentences:

    hops   trots   prowls   soars   bounds

1. The deer —— over the heather.
2. The donkey —— on the sands.
3. The wren —— on the lawn.
4. The lion —— in the forest.
5. The lark —— in the sky.

TEST 4

I. Read very carefully through the following passage, and then answer the questions.

The Three Brothers

The whole of a certain little valley belonged to three brothers called Schwartz, Hans and Gluck. The two elder brothers were very ugly men. They lived by farming the Treasure Valley. They killed everything that did not pay for what it ate. They shot the blackbirds because they pecked the fruit. They killed the hedgehogs in case they worried the cows in the fields. They poisoned the crickets for eating the crumbs in the kitchen. They made the servants work for no wages until they would not work any more, and then they turned them out of doors without paying them. They were so mean and cruel that all who knew them gave them the nickname of the "Black Brothers".

The youngest brother, Gluck, was very different from the others. He was twelve years old, fair, blue-eyed, and kind to everything that was living.

1. What were the names of the three brothers?
2. What did they own?
3. Were the brothers (a) farmers; (b) workers in a factory; (c) cobblers?
4. Which of the brothers were ugly and cruel?
5. Why did they kill the birds and animals around them?
6. They killed the blackbirds by —— them.
7. They killed the crickets by —— them.
8. They paid their servants (a) high wages; (b) nothing at all; (c) very little. Which of these?
9. Why were they called the "Black Brothers"?
10. How was Gluck different from his brothers?

10

II. These words are missing from the story below:

    sparkled   beautiful   prince   thorny
    fountain   garden   beds   lawns

Write out the story, putting them in the correct places.

At last the —— cut his way through the —— hedge and entered the ——. There were trim green ——, and —— flowers were growing in the ——. A —— was playing and its waters —— in the sunlight.

III. Each of the unfinished words in the sentences below ends in **age**. What are these words?

1. The budgerigar had beautiful – – – –**age.**
2. The – – – –**age** on this parcel will not be much.
3. They had a fine meal of bacon and – – – –**age.**
4. The – – – –**age** was loaded into the car.

IV. Rewrite the following sentences choosing the correct words from those given:

1. How did you know it (**was, were**) me?
2. All of you (**is, are**) at fault.
3. The girls (**is, are**) certain to be chosen.
4. None of you (**are, is**) to come.

V. Some words sound the same, but are spelt differently. Here is an example: The (**plane, plain**) flew over the house. The correct word is **plane.** The other word **plain** means 'flat ground'.

1. The miners found iron (**oar, ore**) in the mountains.
2. Things are not what they (**seem, seam**).
3. I'll tell you a (**tail, tale**) of the sea.
4. Sage and (**time, thyme**) grew in the garden.
5. The (**sent, scent**) of roses filled the air.

TEST 5

I. Read very carefully through the following verses, and then answer the questions.

The Pedlar's Caravan

I wish I lived in a caravan
With a horse to drive, like a pedlar-man!
Where he comes from nobody knows,
Or where he goes to, but on he goes.

His caravan has windows two,
And a chimney of tin that the smoke comes through;
He has a wife, and a baby brown,
And they go riding from town to town.

Chairs to mend, and delf to sell!
He clashes the basins like a bell;
Tea-trays, baskets ranged in order,
Plates, with the alphabet round the border.

W. B. Rands

1. Where had the caravan come from? (*a*) No one can tell. (*b*) From the Land of Nod. (*c*) From over the sea from Skye.
2. How did it move from place to place? (*a*) It was a motor-caravan. (*b*) It was drawn by a horse. (*c*) It was a trailer behind a motor-car.
3. What kind of person lived in the caravan: (*a*) a rich merchant; (*b*) a man on holiday; (*c*) a man selling things?
4. How can we tell that he was able to mend broken things?
5. What were the plates like: (*a*) plain white; (*b*) blue all over; (*c*) decorated with letters?
6. Write down the sentences that are **true**: (*a*) The pedlar was married. (*b*) He had to cook outside. (*c*) He had no children. (*d*) He was a bachelor. (*e*) He could make a fire inside the caravan. (*f*) He could see out from the caravan.

II. Look at this: David's tea was **as sweet as** —— . The missing word is **honey**, because the saying is that sweet things are 'as sweet as honey'.

Finish these sentences, using the correct words:

1. The water was **as cold as** —— .
2. Linda was **as quiet as a** —— .
3. Mary's first cake was **as heavy as** —— .
4. After the race, Paul was **as fresh as a** —— .
5. When the holidays began, Martin was **as happy as a** —— .

III. Here are two words, **golf** and **club**. If we put them together we can make a new word **golf-club**.

From these eight words make four new words, using each once only:

night	coal	park	scuttle
hunting	time	horn	keeper

IV. We speak of a **string** of beads. What words might we use to fill these spaces?

1. A —— of grapes.
2. A —— of clothes.
3. A —— of cards.
4. A —— of furniture.
5. A —— of footballers.

V. **Crossword puzzles.**

Here are some crossword-puzzle clues. The answer to each clue begins with QU:

1. Strange and unusual.   QU – – –
2. Where ships sometimes tie up.   QU – –
3. Arrows are carried in this.   QU – – – –
4. When children do not agree.   QU – – – – –
5. Half of a half.   QU – – – – –
6. Reigns over us.   QU – – –

13

TEST 6

I. Read very carefully through the following passage, and then answer the questions.

The Dog and the Bone

A dog who had stolen a juicy bone from a butcher's shop was hurrying into the country where he hoped to enjoy his meal. He came to a bridge that crossed a stream. As he was passing over, he looked down into the water where he saw what he thought was a second dog also carrying a bone. He made up his mind to have that bone as well.

When he stopped, the other dog stopped. When he moved, so did the other. This went on for some time, until the dog on the bridge could stand it no longer. He gave a fierce bark, hoping to scare his enemy. To his dismay, the bone dropped from his own jaws and disappeared below the surface of the stream. When the water cleared, and he looked down, there was the other dog looking up at him. Strangely enough, he had no bone in his jaws.

1. How do we know that the dog had not been **given** the bone as a present?
2. How do we know that the bone was a very fine one?
3. Where was the dog taking the bone to?
4. The dog (a) had to swim across the stream; (b) crossed it with a flying leap; (c) passed over it on a bridge. Which of these is true?
5. Why did he give a fierce bark?
6. What happened when he did this?
7. **To his dismay.** Does this mean (a) he was happy; (b) he was very unhappy; (c) he didn't care very much?
8. Why did the other dog do exactly the same?

II. The sentence 'The key will not fit the lock' means **one** key and **one** lock.   But the sentence 'The **keys** will not fit the **locks**' means **more than one** key and **more than one** lock.

Change the sentences below so that they mean **more than one:**

1. The daisy grew in the hedge.
2. The mouse hid in the wall.
3. The tooth of the tiger shone white.
4. The lady went shopping.
5. He cut his foot on the stone.

III. There are mistakes in each of these sentences.   Write the sentences correctly by changing the wrong word:

1. Mother has gone to lay down.
2. The player done his best.
3. Teasing a cat makes them angry.
4. I cannot find it nowhere.
5. I seen him at the football match.

IV. Write the following sentences, but use **one word** instead of the words in heavy type.

1. This is the **way in.**
2. The coat is **one that keeps out the rain.**
3. The witch was **not able to be seen.**
4. The warder came to **set free** the prisoners.

V. The words **out** and **shout** have the same sound.   We call them **rhyming** words.

Write these eight words in pairs, so that they rhyme:

cheap	route	quest	sleep
queen	pest	scene	boot

TEST 7

I. Read very carefully through the following passage, and then answer the questions.

Great Claus and Little Claus

Once upon a time there lived in a village two men who had the same name, Claus. One of them owned four horses, while the other had only one. So the owner of the four horses was called Great Claus, and the other was known as Little Claus.

All the week Little Claus had to plough for Great Claus, and lend him his one horse. In return, on Sunday, Great Claus would lend Little Claus his four horses. A proud man then was Little Claus. The people looked at him as he brandished his whip over the five horses. He was so pleased that he kept cracking his whip and crying out again and again "Hip, hip, hurrah! Five fine horses and all of them mine!"

"You must not say that," said Great Claus. "Only one of the horses is yours. You know that well enough."

1. How do we know that the two men lived near one another?
2. Why was one called Great Claus, and the other called Little Claus?
3. What were the horses used for?
4. On which days did Little Claus work for Great Claus?
5. Why was Little Claus so happy on Sunday?
6. What did Little Claus shout out that was not true?
7. Why did this make Great Claus angry?
8. Which words in the story tell us that (a) he waved his whip; (b) he made a noise with his whip; (c) everyone was watching him?
9. Which of these makes the best title for the story: (a) The Farmers of England. (b) Little Claus is Careless with his Words. (c) The Happy Brothers.

16

II. In these sentences you will see some short ways of writing words. They are shown in heavy type. Write out these shortened words in full:

1. At the bottom of the page he saw **P.T.O.**
2. Run and call **Dr.** Smith.
3. **Nov.** 30th is **St.** Andrew's Day.
4. Her father is the **Rev.** John Brown.

III. We call **this and that** a word-double. (They talked about **this and that.**)

Finish the word-doubles in the sentences below:

1. The clock's pendulum swung **to and** ——.
2. The box is full of **odds and** ——.
3. Jim landed **safe and** ——.
4. All creatures **great and** —— are welcome.

IV. Here are three sentences from a story, but they are not in the order in which things happened. Write them in the correct order.

1. They were laid in a row on the table.
2. The dolls were taken from the cupboard.
3. The largest and prettiest was then chosen.

V. **Adding a letter.** If we add a letter to PIN, we make the word PINT. In the same way, add a letter to the words below. The letter may be added anywhere in the word.

1. LAP becomes **a jump.**
2. TROT becomes **a fish.**
3. CAP becomes **a piece of land sticking out into the sea.**
4. ASK becomes **something in which liquids are stored.**
5. RAG becomes **anger.**
6. OAT becomes **a vessel.**

17

TEST 8

I. Read very carefully through the following passage, and then answer the questions.

The Crow and the Cheese

A crow one day found a large piece of cheese and flew away with it to a tall tree where she meant to make a meal. A hungry fox passing by saw the crow with the cheese in her beak, and made up his mind to have the tasty food for himself.

"O crow," he said in his gentlest tones, "all the folk of the forest tell me what a charming voice you have, and how very sweetly you sing. Pray, let me hear you warble one of your delightful tunes."

The crow felt very flattered at hearing this praise from the fox, so she opened her beak to sing. At once, the cheese fell to the ground, whereupon the cunning fox grabbed the titbit and hurried away to his den to enjoy his meal, leaving the foolish crow in the treetop, sadder and wiser, and of course hungry.

1. How did the crow come to have the cheese?
2. Where did she go to eat it?
3. When the fox saw the cheese, what did he wish to do?
4. What did he ask the crow to do?
5. When did the cheese fall to the ground?
6. Where did the fox go to have his meal?
7. Why was the crow **sadder and wiser**: (*a*) because she had no one to sing to; (*b*) because the tree had fallen; (*c*) because she had lost the cheese?
8. **The crow was flattered** means (*a*) she was very pleased; (*b*) she was smashed flat by a branch; (*c*) she ate the cheese and grew fat. Which of these?
9. Write down all the words that are used in the story for **the cheese.**

II. The word **big** is the opposite of the word **small.**

Example: Tom was **big** but Jim was **small.**

Write out these sentences using the opposite of the word in heavy type each time to fill the space:

1. The horse was **strong,** but the donkey was —— .
2. The miser is **rich,** but the slave is —— .
3. The troops will **defend** the fort against —— .
4. Why are you so **wise,** and Jack so —— ?

III. Here are the names of eight vegetables. Write them down in **alphabetical order:**

marrow	carrot	parsnip	turnip
bean	swede	onion	leek

IV. **Odd man out.** In each of these groups of words, one word is out of place because it has nothing to do with the others.

Example: girls, lasses, **lads,** maidens. **Lads** is odd man out, because all the others are girls.

Find the **odd man out** in these:

1. cup, saucer, saucepan, plate
2. bicycle, sleigh, sledge, toboggan
3. sword, dagger, shield, lance
4. knife, plate, fork, spoon

V. **This** is to **that.**

Example: **Toe** is to **foot** as **finger** is to —— . Answer: **hand.**

Now do these:

1. **Sty** is to **pig** as **kennel** is to —— .
2. **Vase** is to **flowers** as **scuttle** is to —— .
3. **Stone** is to **solid** as **water** is to —— .
4. **Tall** is to **short** as **fat** is to —— .
5. **Bark** is to **tree** as **feathers** are to —— .

TEST 9

I. Read very carefully through the following passage, and then answer the questions.

The Good Fairy Helps Cinderella

As soon as the Good Fairy waved her wand, the pumpkin became a coach, and the six white mice became ponies. It was now time for Cinderella to leave for the Royal Palace where the ball was to be held. The two Ugly Sisters had gone on ahead, not dreaming that Cinderella would follow. They thought that she would be sitting sadly at the hearth, or doing the cleaning.

When Cinderella walked down the marble staircase, the Prince's eyes opened wide in surprise. Never had he seen such a beautiful damsel. He crossed the ballroom and, bowing low before her, he asked her to dance with him. The band struck up a tune. The handsome Prince and the beautiful maiden waltzed happily round the room, while the onlookers gazed in wonder. Whoever could this be who had stolen the heart of their Prince Charming?

1. Where was the ball taking place?
2. When did the pumpkin become a coach?
3. What had the horses once been?
4. **The band struck up a tune.** Did the men (a) begin to fight; (b) go on strike for more pay; (c) begin to play music?
5. Why was the girl called **Cinderella**: (a) because it was her job to look after the fires; (b) because she was dark in colour, like a cinder; (c) because she lived in a country called Cinderella?
6. Write down the sentences that are **true**: (a) The staircase was made of wood. (b) No one knew who Cinderella was. (c) The Prince took no notice of her. (d) The staircase was a stone one. (e) The Prince asked Cinderella to dance with him. (f) The people looking on knew who Cinderella was.
7. Find words that mean (a) girl; (b) fireside; (c) people looking on.

20

II. The words in the following are in wrong order. Rearrange them to make sentences.

1. The tree Jack climbed tall.
2. Peter the goal scored only.
3. Let me mother it take.
4. Outer man came from space the.

III. These words are missing from the story below:

    gazed   wondered   thick   sign
    happen   moon   rocket   craters

Write the words in the correct spaces.

The —— was now near to the ——. Nothing could be seen but ——. There was no —— of life. The men —— through the —— glass and —— what would —— next.

IV. Look at these little words: **at, in, into, behind, beside.** Write the correct one in the space in each sentence below.

1. The friends sat —— one another.
2. The plane fell —— the sea.
3. The book was —— the cupboard.
4. Sally shot —— the target.
5. In the race, Roger was just —— the winner.

V. Look at the four letters R S A T. With these four letters we can make different words:

1. It twinkles in the sky.
2. Another name for sailors.
3. There were many in Hamelin Town.

   Do the same with these four letters—T S O P.

4. We spin these.
5. —— and pans.
6. This stands in the ground.

TEST 10

I. Read very carefully through the following verses, and then answer the questions.

Queen Mab

A little fairy comes at night,
Her eyes are blue, her hair is brown,
With silver spots upon her wings;
And from the moon she flutters down.

She has a little silver wand,
And when a good child goes to bed,
She waves her wand from right to left
And makes a circle round its head.

And then it dreams of pleasant things,
Of fountains filled with fairy fish;
And trees that bear delicious fruit,
And bow their branches at a wish.

Thomas Hood

1. Where does the little fairy come from?
2. The poem says: (*a*) She rides on a moth's back. (*b*) She travels on a broomstick. (*c*) She flies down. Which of these?
3. Are her wings (*a*) quite plain in colour; (*b*) decorated with silver spots; (*c*) marked in gold and green stripes?
4. For what purpose does she use the wand: (*a*) to ride upon; (*b*) to beat time to the music; (*c*) to weave her magic spells?
5. Write down the sentences that are **true**: (*a*) The child dreams of lovely things. (*b*) The wand is waved up and down. (*c*) The fountains are filled with frogs and toads. (*d*) The wand is waved from right to left. (*e*) The child has horrid dreams. (*f*) There are pretty fish in the fountains.
6. What do the trees do to make the child happy: (*a*) give him shade; (*b*) bring their branches low so that he can reach the fruit; (*c*) give him wood for his bonfire?

II. Write these sentences, but use **one word** instead of the words that are printed in heavy type:

1. He wrote the letter **with great care.**
2. **By good luck** he saw the sign.
3. Come **at once.**
4. He saw the Roman remains in the **building for storing things of the past.**

III. Write the correct answers to each of these:

1. A **hosier** (*a*) sells garden hose; (*b*) sells stockings and socks; (*c*) sells butter, eggs, etc.
2. A **stationer** (*a*) looks after a railway station; (*b*) always stands still; (*c*) sells pens, ink, writing-paper, etc.
3. A **sculptor** (*a*) carves models from wood or stone; (*b*) grows food for sale; (*c*) collects old books.
4. A **locksmith** (*a*) looks after a prison; (*b*) locks up a man named Smith; (*c*) makes and repairs locks of doors.

IV. Rewrite the following sentences using the correct words from those given:

1. Only one of us (**are, is**) able to come.
2. Jill and Robin (**were, was**) older than the twins.
3. All the apples (**was, were**) green.
4. Pam's doll (**were, was**) broken next day.

V. Look at these two sentences: Dick was **happy.** Bill was **unhappy.** By adding **un** to **happy** the word becomes the exact opposite in meaning.

Do the same with these sentences. To make the opposite in each case, choose from these parts of words: **un, in, dis, im.**

1. I **like** carrots but I —— onions.
2. This chair is **comfortable;** that is —— .
3. Her sum is **correct,** but yours is —— .
4. You think it **possible,** but I think it is —— .

23

TEST 11

I. Read very carefully through the following passage, and then answer the questions.

The Hare and the Tortoise

Once, a hare and a tortoise began to argue as to which of them was the faster. They decided to run a race over a certain distance. Almost as soon as they started, the hare was far ahead and out of sight, whilst the tortoise had gone only a few yards.

The hare now thought he would take things easy. He lay down to have a nap until the tortoise could catch up with him. But the tortoise plodded on and on. The hare overslept and awoke with a start. In the distance he could see the tortoise, who had passed him while he was asleep, very near to the winning-post. He ran with might and main in an effort to be first, but the slow-moving tortoise crawled past the finishing line some yards in front of the much speedier hare.

1. What were the hare and the tortoise quarrelling about?
2. How did they decide to settle the quarrel?
3. Why was the hare far ahead whilst the tortoise had gone only a few yards?
4. Explain why the hare lay down to have a nap?
5. What happened while he was asleep?
6. How do we know that the hare did not really mean to sleep so long?
7. By how much did the tortoise beat the hare?
8. Which words or phrases in the story mean: (*a*) as fast as he could; (*b*) went along very slowly; (*c*) far away; (*d*) made up their minds; (*e*) the place where the race ended?
9. Which of these is **true**? (*a*) Harry Hare beat Tommy Tortoise. (*b*) Runner beats crawler. (*c*) Slow but sure is the winner.

II. Look at this: Peter was **as slow as a** ——. The missing word is **tortoise**, because we often say that slow people or things are like the tortoise.

Finish these sentences, using the correct word:

1. During the games lesson, Susan was **as playful as a** ——.
2. While the teacher was away, the class was **as good as** ——.
3. The footballer marking Bob was **as tall as a** ——.
4. The judge was **as wise as an** ——.
5. Philip was a greedy boy and was **as fat as a** ——.

III. **Chop off its head.** If we chop the first letter off the name of an **animal**—FOX—we get another **animal**—OX. (FOX becomes OX.) Do the same with these.

1. 'To begin' becomes a sort of 'fruit pie'.
2. 'Daring, and full of adventure' becomes 'getting on in years'.
3. 'A number together' (like sheep) becomes 'that which fastens a door'.
4. 'Something we sit on' becomes 'that which grows on our heads'.

IV. **Adding a letter.** If we add a letter to PIN, we make the word SPIN. In the same way, add a letter to the words below. The letter may be added anywhere in the word.

1. TEAM becomes **what is given off when water boils.**
2. PAWN becomes **a sea creature.**
3. WAIT becomes **part of the body where a belt is worn.**
4. PLAN becomes **a level piece of land.**

V. Is it **tion** or **sion**? Write down the complete words in these sentences. Each one ends in **tion** or **sion**:

1. The next lesson will be **dicta** ----.
2. When you are old you will have a **pen** ----.
3. The baron lived in a great **man** ----.
4. I want a work of **fic** ---- from the library.

TEST 12

I. Read very carefully through the following passage, and then answer the questions.

Alice and the White Rabbit (retold)

Alice was very tired of sitting by her sister on the bank, and having nothing to do. Once or twice she had peeped into the book her sister was reading, but it had no pictures in it, "and what is the use of a book," thought Alice, "without pictures!"

Suddenly a white rabbit with pink eyes ran close by her. There was nothing so very remarkable in that. Nor did Alice think it so very much out of the way to hear the rabbit say to itself "Oh dear! Oh dear! I shall be too late!" But when the rabbit took a watch out of its waistcoat pocket, and looked at it, and then hurried on, Alice started to her feet. It flashed across her mind that she had never before seen a rabbit with either a waistcoat pocket, or a watch to take out of it.

1. Alice was (a) tired of reading her book; (b) tired of playing with her doll; (c) tired of doing nothing. Which of these?
2. She was sitting (a) in her mother's garden; (b) on a bench in the park; (c) on a bank in the country. Which of these is true?
3. Why didn't she like the book her sister was reading?
4. Write down the sentences that are **true**: (a) The rabbit was black. (b) It wore a dark green overcoat. (c) It spoke to itself. (d) It scurried along. (e) It carried an umbrella. (f) It strolled calmly along. (g) It wore a waistcoat. (h) It was a white rabbit.
5. By what means did the rabbit tell the time?
6. Alice **started to her feet.** Does this mean (a) she was ready to run in a race; (b) she stood up quickly; (c) she put her shoes and stockings on?

II. Crossword puzzles

Here are some crossword-puzzle clues. What are the answers?

1. To fly into the air.   SO – –
2. Helpless and timid.   WE – –
3. Where the steamer begins its trip.   P – – R
4. We travel along this.   RO – –
5. Grows at the edge of a lake.   RE – –

III. A or an? We write: **a** boy, **a** glass, **an** apple, **an** egg.

Write **a** or **an** in the spaces in the sentences below:

1. —— angry sea beat on —— rocky shore.
2. He saw —— ass and —— zebra.
3. —— hunter shot —— elk.
4. —— accident happened in —— school.

IV. Write down the answers to the following questions:

1. What should I expect to find in a scuttle?
2. What do we call a place where a motor-car is kept?
3. What is the front part of a ship called?
4. What would I expect a caddie to do for me?
5. Where would two boxers fight?

V. What did the teacher mean?

1. He said to Richard, 'It's time you turned over a new leaf.' Did he mean (a) started a new page in the exercise book; (b) got on with the gardening; (c) behaved much better than he had done?

2. He said to a footballer, 'Play the game.' Did he mean (a) play the game fairly and according to the rules; (b) begin the game; (c) get on with the game?

3. He said to Brian, 'You've put your foot in it.' Did he mean (a) tried the water in the swimming-pool; (b) stepped into a cage; (c) given himself away, or done something foolish?

27

TEST 13

I. Read very carefully through the following passage, and then answer the questions.

The Woodman's Axe

A poor woodman one day was cutting a tree on the bank of a river. By chance his iron axe slipped from his hand, fell into the water and sank immediately. The woodman sat down and began to cry about his loss. The god who lived in the river, feeling sorry for him, dived to the bottom and brought up a golden axe. But the honest woodman said that it was not his. The river-god dived again and this time brought up a silver axe; but again the woodman refused to take it.

After a third dive into the water the river-god brought up the iron axe. "That is mine," cried the woodman, in great delight. The river-god was so pleased with the truthful way in which the man had behaved that he gave him the gold and silver axes also. The woodman went home to his cottage rejoicing.

1. Where did all this take place: (*a*) in the woodman's garden; (*b*) on a mountain-top; (*c*) near a river?
2. What happened to the woodman's axe?
3. The woodman was helped by (*a*) his friend, who was a woodman; (*b*) the river-god; (*c*) the police. Which of these is true?
4. After which dive did the river-god bring up the woodman's axe?
5. How was the woodman rewarded for being honest?
6. The river-god brought up the other axes because: (*a*) he did not know the difference between them and the iron axe; (*b*) he wanted to know how honest the man was; (*c*) he did not care very much what happened. Which of these?
7. The woodman was: honest, poor, cunning, well-to-do, sly, artful, truthful, straightforward. Write down the words that are true.

II. **How they did it.** We can say 'John behaved **in a stubborn way**', or we can say 'John behaved **like a mule**'. (A mule is a stubborn animal.)

Instead of the words in heavy type in the sentences below, write one of these: like a lamb; like a pig; like a lion; like a tortoise; like a fox.

1. The captain fought **in a very brave way.**
2. The thief behaved **in a very cunning way.**
3. He ate his food **in a very greedy way.**
4. He went to school **in a very slow way.**
5. She went out **in a very quiet way.**

III. **Sound-words.** These are words which when spoken aloud give you some idea of their meaning. Write sound-words in the spaces below:

The —— of the wind and the —— of the torrent were louder than the —— of feet. Nobody heard the —— of the bow, or the —— of the arrow.

IV. **Choosing suitable words.**
1. Here are four **naming words**: plume, seat, road, voice.

Here are four **describing words**: hoarse, waving, comfortable, major.

Put the **naming words** and the **describing words** together in suitable pairs.
2. Now, do the same with these: bloodthirsty, offside, lovely, hidden.

Here are the naming words: princess, goal, pirate, wreck.

V. **He's** in a sentence means **he is.** He's a big lad.
What do the following mean:

that's	who've	o'er
doesn't	o'clock	'tis

TEST 14

I. Read very carefully through the following passage, and then answer the questions.

Jack in Trouble

Jack lived with his widowed mother in a small cottage on the edge of a wood. They were very poor, and had to sell all their possessions in order to get food. The time came when all they had left to sell was a cow. Jack was told to drive the cow to market and sell her for as good a price as he could possibly get.

He set off, but he had not gone very far before he met a man who offered to buy the cow. But he did not offer Jack money. He offered a handful of beans, and simple Jack accepted them, giving the cow in exchange. When he reached home again, you can well believe how angry his mother was. She was so furious that she snatched the beans from the boy and threw them out of the window.

1. Write down the sentences that are **true**: (a) Jack and his mother were wealthy. (b) They lived in a tiny cottage. (c) Jack's father lived with them. (d) They were very poor indeed. (e) Their home was in a large town. (f) Jack's father was dead.
2. What had happened to all their goods?
3. What was Jack going to do with the cow?
4. What was he offered for the cow?
5. Why was his mother so angry when he reached home?
6. Which of these things did she do? (a) She asked him to give her the beans. (b) She snatched the beans from him. (c) She took the beans to market.
7. (a) The beans made a tasty meal. (b) The beans were flung through the window. (c) The beans were planted in the garden. Which is true?
8. Jack was: foolish, clever, wise, stupid, simple, careful, keen. Which of these words are true of Jack?

30

II. Look at this word—**big**. Now look at the three words inside the bracket—(ugly, large, broken). The word nearest in meaning to **big** is **large**.

In the same way, choose a word from those in brackets, in the following:

1. **joke**   (song, book, jest)
2. **timid** (shy, bold, cheeky)
3. **bright** (dull, worn, shining)
4. **rip**   (mend, lose, tear)
5. **new**   (old, modern, broken)

III. Here are the names of eight fish. Write them in **alphabetical order**:

pike	plaice	haddock	eel
cod	herring	whiting	trout

IV. Some words sound the same but are spelt differently. Here is an example: Corn grew on the (**plains, planes**). The correct word is **plains**. The other word **planes** means 'aeroplanes', or 'tools for woodwork'.

Choose the correct word each time:

I had an aunt who went on a (**crews, cruise**) to find a rare (**flower, flour**) for her garden. Soon she (**new, knew**) that the ship had (**missed, mist**) its way in the (**missed, mist**).

V. Choose, from the words in brackets, the most suitable word to finish the lines in this poem:

> A little bit of blowing,
> A little bit of snow,
> A little bit of (**waiting, planting, growing**),
> And crocuses will (**spring, show, leap**);
> On every twig that's lovely,
> A new green leaf will spring,
> On every patient tree-top,
> A thrush will stop and (**chant, sing, warble**).

31

TEST 15

I. Read very carefully through the following verses, and then answer the questions.

The Merry Mice

The merry mice stay in their holes
And hide there all the day;
But when the house is still at night,
The rogues come out and play.

They climb upon the pantry shelf,
And taste of all they please;
They drink the milk that's set for **cream**,
And nibble bread and cheese.

But if they chance to hear the cat,
Their feast will soon be done;
They scamper off to hide themselves
As fast as they can run.

Poet Unknown

1. When do the mice come out?
2. Where have they been all day?
3. What do they have for their supper?
4. How do we know that the things they eat are not on the floor?
5. What happens when they hear the cat coming? (*a*) They stand and make fun of her. (*b*) They change into lumps of cheese. (*c*) They run away in terror.
6. **The milk set for cream,** means: (*a*) the milk left to catch the mice; (*b*) the milk in cream-coloured pans; (*c*) the milk that has been put into pans for making cream. Which of these?
7. Why are the mice merry: (*a*) because someone has been telling them jokes; (*b*) because they can now come out from their hiding-places; (*c*) because bells are ringing?
8. **Their feast will soon be done,** means (*a*) they will wait until they have finished; (*b*) they will scurry away before they have finished; (*c*) the cat will join in the feast. Which is true?

II. The word **low** is the opposite of the word **high.** Write the following sentences using the opposite of the word in heavy type:

1. Shall it be **war** or —— between us? ◌
2. The river is **deep** here, so find a —— place.
3. Shall we stay here and **defend,** or shall we —— ?
4. I thought you were my **friend,** but you are my ——.
5. They sought the treasure **near** and ——.

III. **He** and **his** are words that have to do with MEN or MALE ANIMALS. **Her** and **hers** are words that have to do with WOMEN or FEMALE ANIMALS. In the following sentences, change the words in heavy type so that the animals are FEMALE and not MALE.

1. The **lion** roared in the jungle.
2. The **bull** was sent to market.
3. The **gander** swam on the pond.
4. The **drake** was fed each morning.

IV. **Punctuation marks** (. , ?) are missing from the following sentences. Write the sentences with the correct marks in them:

1. He asked a boy a girl and a soldier
2. Have you eggs and butter
3. Which will you have this or that
4. Were the hammer saw and nails still there

V. **Odd man out.** In each of these groups of words, one word is out of place because it has nothing to do with the others.

Example: dog, cat, lorry, cow. **Lorry** is odd man out because the other three are animals.

Find the **odd man out** in these:

1. waistcoat, boot, plimsoll, shoe
2. poker, tongs, saw, shovel
3. liner, tanker, tug, coach
4. toffee, caramel, biscuit, fruit-drop

TEST 16

I. Read very carefully through the following passage, and then answer the questions.

The Magic Trunk

It was a curious trunk. When the lock was pressed close the trunk would fly. The merchant's son crouched down inside, pressed the lock, and lo! up flew the trunk through the chimney into the clouds, on and on, higher and higher. The lower part was cracked, which rather frightened him, for if it had broken in two, he would have had a nasty fall.

However, it descended safely, and he found himself in Turkey. He hid the trunk under a heap of dry leaves in a wood, and walked into the next town. He could do so very well for, among the Turks, everybody goes about clad as he was, in dressing-gown and slippers. He met a nurse carrying a little child in her arms. "Hark ye, Turkish nurse," quoth he. "What palace is that with high windows close by the town?" "The King's daughter dwells there," replied the nurse.

1. What was so strange about the trunk?
2. Who was inside the trunk: (a) a road-sweeper; (b) the son of a merchant; (c) a space-traveller?
3. What happened when he pressed the lock?
4. How do we know that all this began inside a room?
5. Why was he rather frightened?
6. The trunk came down (a) far away on the ocean; (b) in a foreign country; (c) on another planet. Which of these?
7. Where was the trunk hidden?
8. What clothes was the traveller wearing?
9. Why didn't anyone think his clothes strange?
10. He met (a) a great band of soldiers; (b) a nurse with a baby; (c) some boys from school. Which of these?

II. We speak of a **pair** of shoes. What words might we use to fill these spaces?

1. A —— of firewood.
2. A —— of sardines.
3. A —— of chocolates.
4. A —— of radishes.

III. Each of the answers to the following clues begins with the letters CAN:

1. A Red Indian boat.   CAN – –
2. A bird that sings sweetly.   CAN – – –
3. Used in warfare.   CAN – – –
4. Barges sail on this.   CAN – –
5. He eats human flesh.   CAN – – – – –
6. A sweetmeat.   CAN – –
7. Gives a light.   CAN – – –

IV. The three words in the first bracket all have a similar meaning. Choose **one word** from those in the second bracket which is similar in meaning to those in the first bracket:

Example: (**aid, support, help**)—(**assist**, paint, destroy)

1. (friend, playmate, comrade)—(enemy, companion, uncle)
2. (gap, chink, opening)—(fence, hole, hedge)
3. (lock, bolt, bar)—(cord, chain, cover)
4. (litter, lumber, waste)—(rubbish, food, goods)

V. Here are three sentences from a story, but they are not in the order in which things happened:

1. The switch was pressed, and the rocket took off.
2. The door of the rocket was fastened tightly.
3. It soared away into the blue sky.

Write the sentences in the order in which things took place.

TEST 17

I. Read very carefully through the following passage, and then answer the questions.

The Fishing Competition

The pier was crowded with young people waiting for the competition to begin. At last, the flag was hoisted, and everyone rushed to get to the best position. Splash! splash! Over went the lines. Soon, every fisherman was trying to watch his own float bobbing up and down on the water, and the floats of those around him.

There was a shout of joy, and Mike began to pull in his line. Was it a plaice or a dab on the end? Alas! it was only a bunch of seaweed that had caught on his hook. Sadly, he threw it back. Now the fun really began, as live catches were hauled up, and the little heaps of slithering, slippery fish began to grow in size. Some anglers could hardly wait to bait the hook with a wriggling worm. Time was going on!

1. Who was the competition for: (*a*) people of all ages; (*b*) adults only; (*c*) boys and girls?
2. (*a*) There were many competitors. (*b*) No one turned up. (*c*) Very few people were there. Which of these is true?
3. Where was the event taking place?
4. What was the signal for beginning the competition?
5. (*a*) What did Mike haul up? (*b*) What might it have been?
6. Mike (*a*) was very happy indeed; (*b*) did not care very much; (*c*) was very disappointed. Which?
7. When caught, the fish were (*a*) put into cans; (*b*) laid in heaps on the pier; (*c*) thrown back into the sea. Which of these?
8. Some anglers were (*a*) taking their time over things; (*b*) hurrying to get on with the fishing; (*c*) sitting down and doing nothing. Which of these?

II. Write down the answers to the following questions:

1. What would you expect to find in a sheath?
2. What is the name of a place where young plants are grown?
3. In which game might someone say "Crown this"?
4. What does a coastguard do?
5. Where would a game of tennis be played?

III. Write these sentences, but use **one word** instead of the group of words in heavy type:

1. Hans **lived in Holland.** Hans was —— .
2. He had **no parents.** He was an —— .
3. He was often **in need of food and water.** He was often —— and —— .
4. He had **no friends.** He was —— .

IV. **What do they mean?**

1. Paul said, 'The dinner makes my mouth water.' Did he mean (a) I must wash before dinner; (b) there is only water for dinner; (c) it is such a nice dinner that I can hardly wait to begin?

2. The teacher said, 'You will get into hot water.' Did he mean (a) you must have a bath; (b) you will get into trouble over something; (c) put the hot water into the teapot?

3. Mother said, 'Jane is hanging her head.' Did she mean (a) Jane is making part of a puppet; (b) Jane is preparing a dinner of sheep's head; (c) Jane is sorry for what she has done?

V. These words are missing from the story below:

time	masters	reading	stables
library	story	bad	horse

Mary liked —— 'Black Beauty', a book she had borrowed from the —— . It was the —— of a —— who had several —— , some good and some —— . The horse slept in many different —— as —— went on.

TEST 18

I. Read very carefully through the following passage, and then answer the questions.

A Promise of Treasure

A soldier was marching along the highroad. He had a knapsack on his back, and a sword by his side, for he had been to the wars and was now returning home. On the road he met an old witch, and a very horrid creature she was.

"Good evening, Soldier!" said she. "What a bright sword, and what a large knapsack! You shall have as much money for yourself as you wish."

"Thanks, old Witch!" cried the soldier.

"Do you see yonder large tree?" said the Witch, pointing to one that stood close by. "It is quite hollow within. Climb up to the top, and you will find a hole large enough for you to creep through, and thus you will get into the tree. I will tie a rope round your waist so that I can pull you up again when you call me."

1. Where was the soldier coming from?
2. Name two things which he was carrying.
3. The soldier was (a) travelling on horseback; (b) riding on a motor-cycle; (c) marching along. Which of these?
4. How do we know that the witch whom he met was not a pleasant person?
5. When did the meeting take place: (a) in the early morning; (b) some time after tea; (c) in the afternoon?
6. What did the witch offer to give to the soldier?
7. Why was it that the soldier was able to get into the tree?
8. How did the witch promise to get the soldier up again?
9. Which of these would make a good name for the story? (a) The Soldier Meets an Old Army Friend. (b) A Meeting with a Strange, Old Creature. (c) The Soldier Arrives Home Safely.

II. The words **trees** and **please** both have the same sound. They are rhyming words.

Write these eight words in pairs, so that they rhyme:

dough	scythe	mow	lime
climb	plaice	blithe	base

III. Look at these four letters: E T A M. With them we can make several words:

1. Not wild.
2. Eleven of these make a football ——— .
3. The flesh of animals.

Now make words with these four letters: A E S T.

4. Opposite of west.
5. We sit on this.
6. '———, light refreshments and minerals.'

IV. The word **wave** has more than one meaning. It may mean 'the **wave** on the **seashore**'; or it may mean 'the **wave** of the **hand**'.

Write down the words that can mean:

1. A large case or box, like that belonging to Captain Billy Bones; part of everyone's body.
2. Used to stop the sun from shining through the window; unable to see.
3. Used for lifting heavy weights; a bird with long legs.
4. Part of the sea coast, sometimes sandy; the noise made by a bloodhound.

V. Here are some **crossword-puzzle clues.** What are the answers?

1. A vegetable.   LE – –
2. A horse and a lion have one.   MA – –
3. What the conductor shouts.   'FA – – – please.'
4. Beef, pork and mutton.   ME – –

TEST 19

I. Read very carefully through the following passage, and then answer the questions.

The Changing of the Guard

John went to see the Changing of the Guard, and stood in the crowd outside Buckingham Palace. The tall guardsmen in their scarlet tunics came marching along; their black bearskins made them seem even taller. The band played a lively tune, and everyone's feet went tap-tap-tapping in time to the music. The officers' swords gleamed in the sunshine, and so did the soldiers' bayonets and buttons. The men looked just like toy soldiers from a wooden box. Orders were shouted and obeyed smartly.

John wondered whether the Queen was up there at one of the high windows, watching her guardsmen. He saw a curtain move, but he was not near enough to see if it were Her Majesty.

Soon the Changing of the Guard was over. The crowd melted away, and John went home to lunch.

1. Where did the Changing of the Guard take place?
2. What other words are used for: (*a*) the Queen; (*b*) the soldiers?
3. What three things were shining in the sunlight?
4. What was John wondering while this was going on?
5. What made the soldiers seem very tall indeed? (*a*) They were marching on the pavement. (*b*) The people looking on were dwarfs. (*c*) They wore tall black hats.
6. How do we know that there was music to be heard?
7. How do we know this was happening (*a*) in the morning; (*b*) in London?
8. **The crowd melted away.** Does this mean (*a*) the people all disappeared; (*b*) they walked away; (*c*) they really melted?

II. 'John lives in **Oakwood Pl.**' **Pl.** is short for **Place.**
Write these in full:

1. Sheila lives in Princes **Rd.**
2. Stephen lives in George **St.**
3. Joy lives in Grange **Gdns.**
4. Susan lives in Wood **Ave.**
5. Tony lives in Hope **Sq.**

III. **Proper nouns.** All proper nouns (special names) begin with
a **capital letter.**

Rewrite these sentences, beginning each proper noun with a
capital letter:

1. peter smith is a pupil at loamshire primary school.
2. His teacher is mr. rogers.
3. The river thames flows near by.

IV. John, Anne, Michael and Jean are all **names.** Write **one
word** for each of the following groups:

1. spring, summer, autumn, winter
2. Monday, Tuesday, Wednesday, Friday
3. Mars, Venus, Jupiter, Saturn
4. silk, nylon, tweed, velvet
5. coal, coke, peat, paraffin

V. From the words **inside the bracket** in each sentence, write down
the one which is nearest in meaning to the word in front of the
sentence.

Example: **level.** The ground was (bumpy, swampy, **flat**).

1. **curious** What a (mean, strange, happy) thing to do.
2. **modern** That carving is (new, ugly, old).
3. **mariner** The (explorer, seaman, native) walked on the quay.
4. **dusk** They were home by (morning, twilight, midday).

TEST 20

I. Read very carefully through the following verses, and then answer the questions.

Spring

I am coming, I am coming!
Hark! the little bee is humming.
See the lark is soaring high
In the blue and sunny sky;
And the gnats are on the wing,
Wheeling round in airy ring.

See the yellow catkins cover
All the slender willows over;
And on banks of mossy green
Star-like primroses are seen;
And their clustering leaves below,
White and purple violets blow.

Mary Howitt

1. Who is saying 'I am coming': (*a*) the Fairy Queen; (*b*) the season of Spring; (*c*) Old Man Winter?
2. Here are some colours used in the poem: blue, yellow, green, purple. Write them with the correct nouns from this list: violets, catkins, sky, banks.
3. Write down the words that tell us what each of these is doing: (*a*) The bee is ——. (*b*) The lark is ——. (*c*) The gnats are ——.
4. How can we tell that it was a warm and pleasant day?
5. Why do you think the primroses were said to be star-like?
6. Write down the sentences that are **true**: (*a*) The violets were all of one colour. (*b*) There were many leaves, in bunches. (*c*) It was easy to see the violets. (*d*) The leaves were few in number. (*e*) There were violets of two colours. (*f*) The violets were half hidden. (*g*) The lark was flying high in the sky. (*h*) The willows had no catkins on them.

II. Sound-words. Write sound-words in the spaces in the sentences below:

The ——— of broken glass followed the ——— of the bullet as the rifle ——— . The soldiers were awakened by the ——— of the bugle.

III. Choosing suitable words.

1. Here are four **nouns**: elf, mountain, bird, eel.

And here are four other words, one to **describe** each of the words above: feathered, snow-capped, tiny, wriggling.

Put the **nouns** and the **describing words** together in suitable pairs.

2. Now do the same with these words: dainty, fierce, barking, sugary.

Here are the **nouns**: tea, bull, dog, sprite.

IV. Finish these proverbs, or well-known sayings:

1. A miss is as good as ——— ——— .
2. Don't count your chickens ——— ——— ——— ——— .
3. Look before ——— ——— .
4. A friend in need ——— ——— ——— ——— .

V. Look at these sentences.

    1. The boy came first.   2. He is young.

We can make them into one sentence by using the word **who.** We can write 'The boy **who** came first is young.'

Join each of the sentences below by using **who, which, whose** or **whom.**

1. This is the cap.   It is torn.
2. I am the boy.   You saw me.
3. He is the soldier.   His rifle was stolen.
4. I saw the tramp.   He called yesterday.

TEST 21

I. Read very carefully through the following passage, and then answer the questions.

Holiday Plans

In March, the family sat down at the table and began to talk about the summer holiday. Where should they go this year? That was the question which had to be answered. Should they go to the seaside, or to the country? Did they prefer fun on the farm, or basking on a beach? The children soon settled that. With one voice they cried, "Seaside, please!"

"Let's go somewhere where there's good swimming," said Sally, who had just won her Life-Saving Certificate. "And good fishing," said Alan, who had been given a smart rod for his birthday. "What about mountain climbing?" Paul asked. He had been to Switzerland, the year before, with the Scout troop.

"Mother and I just want to sit on a beach," said Father, "that is, if you don't mind, of course."

"Two deck-chairs for a fortnight for Mother and Father. Then everyone will be happy," the children cried.

1. Why was the family holding the meeting?
2. What two kinds of places did they first think about?
3. Which did they decide upon?
4. **Basking on a beach** means (*a*) climbing up a tree; (*b*) lying in the sun at the seaside; (*c*) sitting in a basket chair. Which of these?
5. Why was Sally keen on swimming?
6. Why was Alan keen to fish?
7. Why did Paul want to go mountain climbing?
8. Why did the children say "Two deck-chairs for Mother and Father": (*a*) because their parents always sit in deck-chairs; (*b*) because they were going for a sail on a boat; (*c*) because their parents wanted to sit on the beach and rest?

II. Write down the names of these people whom we meet in books and poems:

1. He was a merry old soul.
2. He clung tightly to Sinbad the Sailor's back, and wouldn't let go.
3. Her mother was afraid that she would be late for school.
4. He sailed away in a wooden spoon with Wynken and Blynken.
5. He fished in his mother's washing tub.

III. **Chop off its head.** If we chop the first letter off **a place where we go skating**—RINK, we get **something we use when writing**—INK. (RINK becomes INK.)

Do the same with these:

1. 'A place where we play games' becomes 'Noah's ship'.
2. 'A sea vessel' becomes 'a part of the body'.
3. 'Something we open to go into the garden' becomes 'what we did with our food at our last meal'.
4. 'Part of the foot' becomes 'a wriggling fish'.
5. 'A wild beasts' den' becomes 'that which we breathe'.
6. 'One who cleans chimneys' becomes 'to cry'.

IV. In each case, rearrange the letters of the words below to make the name of a **bird.**

Example: WAKH becomes HAWK.

1. WORC	2. REWN	3. NERT
4. NAWS	5. CKDU	6. KRAL

V. Read through this passage very carefully and then write it down, as it should be written, in verse. Begin each line with a **capital letter.**

Now to the banquet we press, now for the eggs and the ham, now for the mustard and cress, now for the strawberry jam.

TEST 22

I. Read very carefully through the following passage, and then answer the questions.

The Racing Car

The boys first chose a soap-box for the body. They took four wheels from an old pram on a rubbish heap, found some long nails and a length of rope, and they were ready to begin building the racing car. There were many mistakes, and sore fingers, before the Silver Arrow was ready for its trial run. They hauled it to the top of a steep slope, climbed aboard and pushed off.

The car gathered speed and went rushing downwards. All was well for the first minute. Then, Jack gasped "The bend at the bottom!" Yes, they had forgotten all about the great curve. It was coming nearer, nearer. There was not the slightest chance of steering the Silver Arrow at that speed. With a screeching sound it left the road and burst through the wire fence.

1. What was the body of the car made of: (*a*) an old pram; (*b*) an empty soap-box; (*c*) part of a real motor-car?
2. Where were the wheels found?
3. How were the parts fastened together?
4. Why were there sore fingers: (*a*) because the boys were biting their nails; (*b*) because they had hit their hands with the hammer; (*c*) because they had burnt them?
5. Where did the boys go to test the car?
6. (*a*) It went quicker and quicker. (*b*) The car refused to start. (*c*) It overturned at the start. Which of these is true?
7. What did Jack suddenly remember?
8. (*a*) The car ran into a lorry. (*b*) It ran on to the pavement. (*c*) It crashed through a fence at the side of the road. Which of these is true?

II. Some words sound the same, but are spelt differently. Here is an example: The old (**which, witch**) flew away on her broomstick. The correct word is **witch.**

Rewrite the following sentences using the correct words from those given:

1. He tried in (**vain, vane**) to find the treasure.
2. He tramped over many a hill and (**veil, vale**).
3. He (**herd, heard**) many stories of where it was hidden.
4. At last he saw a coloured (**buoy, boy**) floating on the sea.

III. Look at this word—**broad.** Now look at the three words inside this bracket—(wide, narrow, empty). The word nearest in meaning to **broad** is **wide,** so we choose that. **Broad**—**wide.**

Do the same with these, choosing one word each time.

1. **peasant**   (explorer, countryman, footballer)
2. **ship**   (vase, scuttle, vessel)
3. **brook**   (river, stream, ocean)
4. **field**   (meadow, jungle, heath)
5. **throw**   (catch, taste, hurl)

IV. The word **hot** is the opposite of the word **cold.** Write the following sentences using the opposite of the word in heavy type:

1. Your wood is **smooth,** and his is —— .
2. They travelled over **land** and —— .
3. It is a question of **right** and —— .
4. The magic rose bloomed in **winter** and —— .
5. The sun shines **often;** the wind blows —— .

V. Choose, from the words in brackets, the most suitable word to finish the lines in this poem:

> Sing hey! Sing hey!
> For Christmas (**eve, day, morn**);
> Twine mistletoe and holly,
> For friendship grows
> In winter (**time, months, snows**),
> And so let's all be (**merry, happy, jolly**).

TEST 23

I. Read very carefully through the following passage, and then answer the questions.

Tony's Travels

There were three ways in which Tony could travel to school: by bus, by steam train or on the underground railway. Each of these ways held something special. The bus journey was interesting because one passed shops and markets, human beings, traffic lights, other buses and cars. The steam train was exciting because one could run up and down the corridor—if the guard wasn't on the prowl, as he usually was, knowing what a naughty cargo he was carrying.

The underground train was the quickest. Tony used this only if he had something important to do when he reached school—something that had to be done, unpleasant though it might be, such as finishing last night's homework. The fare to Goodhampton was exactly the same whichever way he travelled.

1. How do we know that Tony lived some distance away from his school?
2. What were the three ways of travelling?
3. Which journey cost the most?
4. Why was Tony happy when he travelled by bus?
5. Why did the guard have to **prowl** about in the train?
6. Which was the quickest way of travelling?
7. Why did Tony sometimes go by underground?
8. In what town was Tony's school?
9. From this list choose words that describe the journey (*a*) by bus; (*b*) by train; (*c*) by underground.

    quick   attractive   speedy   thrilling
    enchanting   rapid   fast   uninteresting

II. Odd man out. In each of these groups of words, one word is out of place because it has nothing to do with the others.

Example: cow, horse, **lion**, sheep. **Lion** is odd man out, because all the others are tame animals.

Find the **odd man out** in these:

1. bacon, pork, beef, ham
2. carrot, chop, steak, kidney
3. carpet, settee, shirt, rug
4. coffee, cocoa, lemonade, tea

III. Look at this sentence: This is **Susans** doll. There is something missing—an **apostrophe**—to show that the doll belongs to Susan. It should have been: This is **Susan's** doll.

Write the **apostrophe** in its place in these sentences:

1. I went to Betty Browns party.
2. I am David Copperfields aunt.
3. Where is Oliver Twists gruel?
4. Long John Silvers parrot died.

IV. Look at this sentence: 'Bill **scores** a goal.' It is happening **now.** But if we write 'Bill **scored** a goal', it is written as if it happened **in the past.**

All the sentences below are written as if they are happening **now.** Write them as if they happened **in the past.**

1. Jean **makes** a cake.
2. Mother **cleans** the windows.
3. Father **drives** a car.
4. The hen **lays** an egg.
5. She **sees** the picture.
6. The dog **barks** at the stranger.

V. Write these foods in **alphabetical order:**

cheese	coffee	bacon	bread
biscuits	cocoa	chocolate	butter

TEST 24

I. Read very carefully through the following passage, and then answer the questions.

Jane's Problem

There were half a dozen dolls in the window. They were all on one shelf. Each doll was dressed in the clothes of the country from which it came. There was a Japanese doll in a kimono, and a doll in the grass skirt of Fiji. A third wore the kilt of Scotland, and a fourth had on the tall, black hat of Wales. Next came a Red Indian doll which wore a coloured blanket, and shoes called moccasins. Last of all was the English doll, a neat little girl in school uniform.

It was going to be very hard for Jane to choose one doll from this charming collection. Each had something that made it seem nicer than the others. Yet, only one could be chosen. She had no money for more than one. Was it to be the biggest, or the prettiest?

1. Which of these is true? (*a*) There were many, many dolls. (*b*) There was one doll. (*c*) There were six dolls.
2. Which of these is true? (*a*) They were all dressed alike. (*b*) They were dressed in different kinds of clothes. (*c*) Their clothes could not be seen.
3. What did Jane have to choose?
4. Where was the kimono: (*a*) on the doll's back; (*b*) on her feet; (*c*) on her head?
5. Where were the moccasins: (*a*) on the doll's feet; (*b*) on her back; (*c*) on her head?
6. Here are the countries: Japan, Wales, Scotland, Fiji, England, North America. And here are the clothes: grass skirt, kilt, kimono, black hat, moccasins, school uniform. Put them into their correct pairs.
7. Which doll wore a coloured blanket?

II. The sentence 'The boy used the long nail', means **one** boy and **one** nail. But the sentence 'The **boys** used the long **nails**', means **more than one** boy and **more than one** nail.

Change the sentences below so that they mean **more than one**:

1. The dwarf hid on the shelf.
2. The man drove the car very fast.
3. The sheep fed on the hillside.
4. The gun fired the shell.

III. Here are two words **paper** and **weight.** If we put these together we can make a new word **paper-weight.**

From these eight words make four new words, using each once only:

spoon	sea	tea	mill
gull	knee	water	cap

IV. Finish the sentences below, choosing the correct word from these:

heavy	light	sweet
hard	precious	sour

1. Sugar is —— .
2. Lead is —— .
3. Vinegar is —— .
4. Gold is —— .
5. Cork is ——. .
6. Iron is —— .

V. These words are missing from the story below. Write out the story, using them to fill the spaces.

wanderings	humans	exciting
animals	strange	rabbit-hole

It was an —— book, all about Alice falling down a —— , and of the —— things that happened in her —— underground. Before she awoke from her dream she met many —— who spoke like —— .

TEST 25

I. Read very carefully through the following verses, and then answer the questions.

The Moon

The moon has a face like the clock in the hall;
She shines on thieves on the garden wall,
On streets and fields and harbour quays,
And birdies asleep in the forks of the trees.

The squalling cat and the squeaking mouse,
The howling dog by the door of the house,
The bat that lies in bed at noon,
All love to be out by the light of the moon.

But all of the things that belong to the day
Cuddle to sleep to be out of the way;
And flowers and children close their eyes,
Till up in the morning the sun shall rise.

R. L. Stevenson

1. Why has the moon a face like the clock in the hall: (*a*) because it is seen only at night; (*b*) because they both make a ticking sound; (*c*) because it is round, like a clock-face?
2. Why are the birdies asleep **in the forks of the trees:** (*a*) because they are safer there; (*b*) because they have had no supper; (*c*) because they are afraid of the moon?
3. Finish these sentences with **sound-words** from the poem: (*a*) The cat is —— . (*b*) The dog is —— . (*c*) The mouse is —— .
4. What are **harbour quays:** (*a*) the keys that open the harbour; (*b*) places where ships can tie up; (*c*) the streets of the town?
5. The bat is in its bed at —— o'clock. Finish this sentence.
6. What are sleeping at night?
7. What will wake them up?
8. Choose a new title for the poem from: (*a*) All the Fun of the Fair. (*b*) A Dangerous Voyage. (*c*) When Day is Done.

II. There are mistakes in each of the following sentences. Write the sentences correctly:

1. The work was did too quickly.
2. Give me them sweets at once.
3. The cat was laying on the roof.
4. Whose toys is those?
5. The book fell off of the table.

III. We call **neck** and **neck** a word-double. (They finished the race **neck** and **neck.**)

Finish the word-doubles in the following sentences:

1. He shouted **again and** —— .
2. I shall come **by and** —— .
3. The boy rolled **over and** —— .
4. The top spun **round and** —— .

IV. Look at the four letters E D R A. With these four letters we can make several words:

1. We sometimes begin a letter '—— Sir'.
2. To take a risk.
3. Children sometimes say '—— me a story'.

Now look at these four letters: I V E L. With these four letters we can make:

4. Wicked.
5. She wore a pretty —— on her hat.
6. I hope that the Prince and Princess will —— happily ever after.

V. **I'm** in a sentence means **I am.** **I'm** going out.
What do these mean:

can't	didn't	don't
isn't	there's	I've

TEST 26

I. Read very carefully through the following passage, and then answer the questions.

The Great Adventure

A troop of Boy Scouts was marching down the road. Left, right, left, right—they kept in perfect step. The bugles blared and the drums beat. A flag was carried along. Four brawny lads hauled the big trek-cart that was laden with goods for the camp. There were things to eat and things to drink, things to wear and things to use—a great mixture of flour, lemonade, pails, hats, tea, sugar, ginger-beer, poles and water. All these were separate, of course. It would have been fun if they had suddenly got mixed up together.

At the end of the road three lorries were waiting. The joyful lads piled aboard, and to the sound of singing from half a hundred young voices, the convoy started. The Great Adventure had begun. There were fourteen days ahead, glorious days of fun and frolic.

1. How many Scouts were there: (a) more than one could count; (b) very few; (c) about fifty?
2. How can we tell that the Scouts were marching smartly?
3. What was the **Great Adventure?** Was it (a) going to camp; (b) going to the war; (c) going to school?
4. How were they going to travel: (a) by British Rail; (b) by road, in lorries; (c) by aeroplane?
5. How do we know that there was a band playing?
6. (a) Their goods were carried by hand. (b) They had gone on ahead. (c) They were pulled along in a cart. Which is true?
7. For how long were they going to be away?
8. What were the things (a) to eat; (b) to drink; (c) to wear; (d) to use?

II. Here are three sentences from a story, but they are not in the order in which things happened. Write them in the correct order.
1. The 'plane circled over the city.
2. The pilot climbed into the cockpit of the aeroplane.
3. Parcels of food were dropped to the starving people.

III. Write the correct answers to each of these:

1. A **plumber** (*a*) sells plums; (*b*) mends broken water-pipes; (*c*) sells lumber.
2. A **poacher** (*a*) poaches eggs in a café; (*b*) steals rabbits that belong to other people; (*c*) watches clocks.
3. A **tinker** (*a*) mends kettles and pots; (*b*) drives a tanker; (*c*) spends his time thinking.
4. A **jockey** (*a*) plays a game with a ball and stick; (*b*) rides a horse in a race; (*c*) keeps a shop.

IV. Look at these two sentences: This bridge is **safe.** That is **unsafe.** By adding **un** to **safe** the word becomes the exact opposite in meaning.

Do the same with these sentences: To make the opposite in each case, choose from these parts of words: **un, mis, im, in.**

1. You are very **kind,** but Mary is —— .
2. This way is **direct,** but that is —— .
3. Peter will **behave,** but Paul will —— .
4. Jill is **polite,** but Linda is —— .

V. Rewrite the sentences below, but use single words instead of the words in heavy type:

As the sun **went out of sight** behind the hills, Robin Hood and his band **came into view.** The **men and women who were in chains** hoped that they would soon be **set at liberty,** so that they might return **at once** to their **houses, huts and cottages.**

TEST 27

I. Read very carefully through the following passage, and then answer the questions.

Jolly Roger

Nearer and nearer came the galleon. The crew of the brig found their joy turned to sorrow, for a flag appeared at the mast-head, the hated and feared Jolly Roger. The white skull and crossbones stood out clearly against the black flag.

There was not a moment to lose! The brig's crew sprang to life, and hurried below for weapons. They came on deck again with a mixed collection—cutlasses, pikes, swords, daggers and pistols. The brass gun in the bows was loaded, and the muzzle pointed towards the pirate which was now very near indeed. It was to be a battle between David and Goliath.

No one expected any mercy if they fell into the hands of Fork-Beard and his band of ruffians. Walking the plank! That was the way many a crew had met its fate when captured.

1. Why did the crew of the brig suddenly become very sad?
2. Where did the Jolly Roger fly: (*a*) from a sailor's hands; (*b*) from a porthole; (*c*) from the mast-head?
3. The pirates' flag was (*a*) red, white and blue; (*b*) black, with a skull and crossed bones; (*c*) green, with yellow birds. Which describes it?
4. The crew **sprang to life.** Does this mean (*a*) they had been dead, but came to life; (*b*) they sprang overboard; (*c*) they all rushed to get weapons?
5. (*a*) The weapons were stored below decks. (*b*) They were already in the sailors' hands. (*c*) They were already piled on deck. Which of these is true?
6. Why does a battle between **David and Goliath** tell us that the galleon was much larger than the brig?
7. How were captured sailors often put to death by the pirates?

II. **A** or **An?** We write: **a** song, **a** wolf, **an** otter, **an** egg.

Write **a** or **an** in the spaces in the sentences below:

1. She had —— pretty doll, and —— ugly one.
2. —— underground passage led to —— beach.
3. —— ant and —— bumble bee were caught.
4. Can we change —— Airedale for —— terrier?
5. —— friend of mine eats —— apple or —— pear each day.

III. The word **fine** has more than one meaning. It may mean 'a **fine** we have to pay for doing wrong', or '**fine** weather'.

Write down the words than can mean:

1. Belonging to me; where coal is dug; something floating in the sea, which explodes on striking a ship.
2. Out of harm's way; where valuable things are kept.
3. Not heavy; helps us to see in the darkness.
4. To write one's name at the end of a letter; hangs outside an inn or other building.

IV. Write the correct words to finish these sentences:

1. The aeroplane was left in its **h----r.**
2. They saw the cowboy film at the new **c----a.**
3. They had lunch at a lonely **c--é.**
4. The Roman remains were in the **m----m.**
5. There was a pantomime at the local **t-----e.**

V. The words **he** and **she** both have the same sound. They are rhyming words.

Write these eight words in pairs, so that they rhyme:

through	blue	duty	stuff
clear	tough	queer	beauty

TEST 28

I. Read very carefully through the following passage, and then answer the questions.

In the Depths of the Sea

The giant octopus left its cave, and moved along the reef. Somehow or other the news was flashed to every living thing. Most of them crawled, swam or scuttled for shelter. The smaller fish found cracks and crevices in which to hide. The shrimps and prawns darted here and there in panic, and the crabs and lobsters slithered away to dark corners, to wait until Old Killer had gone.

One alone stayed to do battle. This was the great eel who had long fancied himself against the King of the Reef, and was waiting for a chance to defeat the octopus and take over his crown. The eel depended upon his swift rushes and strong jaws to overcome the eight long arms, each covered with dozens of suckers which could grip an enemy and draw it to the parrot-like beak.

1. Where did all this happen?
2. The octopus has two other names. What are they?
3. What was the bad news that the other creatures soon heard?
4. What did each creature have to do as quickly as possible?
5. Where did the small fish go?
6. What happened to the shrimps and prawns?
7. What did the great eel make up his mind to do?
8. How did the eel win his battles with other fish?
9. What made the octopus such a dangerous enemy to fight?
10. The eel wanted to take over the **octopus's crown.** Does this mean (*a*) he wanted to wear a crown that the octopus was wearing; (*b*) he wanted to dive about in the water; (*c*) he wanted to become King of the Reef?
11. What was the **reef:** (*a*) a pool in the rocks; (*b*) a sandy bank; (*c*) a great ledge of rocks under the sea?

II. Complete these **proverbs,** or well-known sayings:

1. Too many cooks —— —— —— .
2. Where there's a will —— —— —— .
3. More haste —— —— .
4. Early to bed and early to rise —— —— —— —— —— ——
   —— .

III. Jill, Sally, Elizabeth and Jane are all **girls' names.** Give a general name for each of the following groups:

1. pine, fir, spruce, larch
2. car, taxi, coach, carriage
3. trumpet, bugle, drum, triangle
4. King, Queen, Prince, Princess

IV. **Proper nouns.** All proper nouns (special names) begin with a capital letter.

Rewrite these sentences, beginning each proper noun with a **capital letter:**

1. mary finished reading 'treasure island'.
2. She took the book to london with her.
3. She lent it to jane, and received 'billy bunter' instead.
4. The book had been given to jane for christmas.

V. From the words **inside the bracket** in each sentence, write down the one which is nearest in meaning to the word in front of the sentence.

Example: **true.** This is an (idle, **exact,** awkward) story.

1. **chill**   Outside a (pleasant, gentle, cold) wind blew.
2. **brook**   Let us go and fish in the miller's (pond, stream, lake).
3. **sweet**   This tea is too (sugary, bitter, strong).
4. **scholar** I am a (master, pupil, tutor) at the new school.

TEST 29

I. Read very carefully through the following passage, and then answer the questions.

On Private Property

The notice said plainly PRIVATE, KEEP OUT. Each time Tim saw the words they seemed to say "It doesn't mean you; come in." At last he could stand it no longer. He looked up and down the road. There was no one in sight. He scrambled through the ditch, then pushed his way through a hole in the fence and into the wood.

The bushes were wet and thorny, and each one tried to grasp him as he went by. But he pressed on until he found the clearing. There was the black-painted hut. He went towards it carefully, and tried to peep in through a window, but it was boarded up. The door, too, looked solid, and there was no sign of a handle. Suddenly, from inside came the sound of voices.

1. What was painted on the notice-board?
2. (*a*) Tim didn't see the notice. (*b*) Tim did as the notice told him. (*c*) Tim thought it said 'COME IN'. Which of these is true?
3. Why did he look up and down the road?
4. Through what two things did he pass to get inside?
5. The bushes tried to hold him (*a*) because they were thorny; (*b*) because they were very high; (*c*) because they were on fire. Which of these is true?
6. What was **the clearing**: (*a*) a ring of people; (*b*) a place where the trees had been cleared away; (*c*) something he had lost in the bushes?
7. Which of these did he see: (*a*) a tin hut with a thatched roof; (*b*) a fortress; (*c*) a hut that was painted black?
8. Why couldn't he see through the window?
9. What sound came from inside?

II. Rearrange the letters of the words below to make the name of an **insect.**

Example: E B E becomes BEE.

1. A F E L   2. P A W S   3. N T A
4. T A N G   5. T H M O

III. Read very carefully through the following passage, and then write it down, as it should be written, in verse. Begin each line with a **capital letter:**

Now for the tea of our host, now for the raspberry bun, now for the muffin and toast, now for the gay Sally Lunn.

IV. Write down the names of these people whom we meet in books and poems:

1. He climbed a beanstalk.
2. He dressed himself in a cap and coat of goatskin.
3. He ran through the town in his nightgown.
4. He rode from London to York.
5. He comes in the night, he comes in the night.

V. Instead of 'He said **he would** do it', we can write 'He said **he'd** do it.'

Write out the following sentences using short ways of writing the words that are in heavy type:

1. **All is** well that ends well.
2. I **shall not** help you with your homework.
3. **We have** come home.
4. **It is** Christmas Day tomorrow.
5. **There is** a 29 bus in the distance.

TEST 30

I. Read very carefully through the following verses, and then answer the questions.

The Cow

The friendly cow all red and white
I love with all my heart,
She gives me cream with all her might
To eat with apple-tart.

She wanders lowing here and there,
And yet she cannot stray,
All in the pleasant open air,
The pleasant light of day.

And blown by all the winds that pass,
And wet with all the showers,
She walks amid the meadow grass,
And eats the meadow flowers.

R. L. Stevenson

1. Why does the child in the poem love the cow so much: (*a*) because the cow lets him ride on her back; (*b*) because the cow pulls a cart along; (*c*) because the cow gives milk that is made into cream?

2. How do we know that the weather is not **always** warm and pleasant for the cow?

3. How do we know that the cow is not silent while she walks?

4. All this is happening (*a*) on a summer's day; (*b*) in a foggy autumn; (*c*) on a winter's night. Which of these is true?

5. How do we know that the cow is not feeding high up on the mountainside?

6. If Friesian cows are black and white, Jersey cows are light brown, Hereford cows are red and white, and Red Polls are red all over, which is the cow in the poem?

7. Look at these words: friendly, peaceful, savage, kindly, dangerous, fierce, lovable. Write down those which describe the cow.

II. Some words sound the same, but are spelt differently. Here is an example: This is the book (**witch, which**) you need. The correct word is **which.**

Write out this passage choosing the correct words:

The (**seen, scene**) made us (**stare, stair**) in wonder through the (**pane, pain**). The (**tied, tide**) was out, and the ship was gone from the (**pier, peer**).

III. Look at this sentence: 'Bill **makes** a run from the first ball.' It is happening **now.** 'Bill **made** a run from the first ball' means that it happened **in the past.**

Write the following sentences as if they had already happened:

1. The miller **grinds** his corn.
2. Miss Smith **teaches** the children.
3. The airman **flies** over the school.
4. The grass **is** green in the meadows.
5. The birds **nest** in the trees.

V. Look at this sentence: This is Johns bat. The **apostrophe** is missing. The sentence should have been: This is John's bat.

Write out these sentences, putting the **apostrophe** in its correct place.

1. Where is Lucys locket?
2. Come to Black Beautys stable.
3. I am going to the Mad Hatters tea-party.
4. This is Wee Willie Winkies house.

V. Write these in order of size, beginning each time with the smallest:

1. football, golf ball, bowl, tennis ball
2. eagle, sea-gull, blue tit, starling
3. peke, Alsatian, bulldog, St. Bernard
4. butterfly, dragon-fly, bee, ant